Mia G. Pickeras

# GRUMPY CAT®
## NO -IT -ALL

5th grade

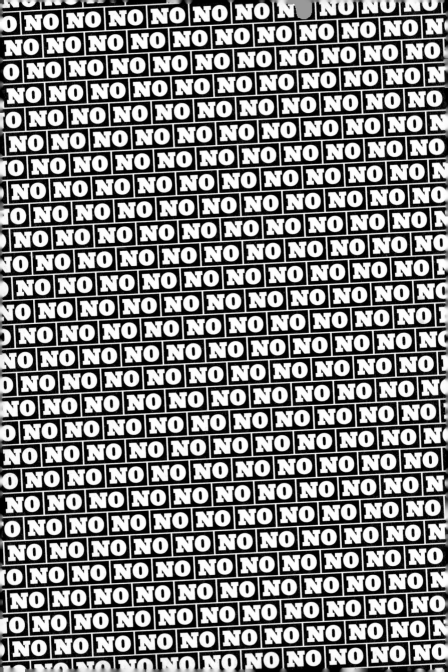

# GRUMPY CAT®

## NO -IT -ALL

EVERYTHING YOU NEED TO KNOW

SCHOLASTIC INC.

## NO Thanks to:

Bryan, Tabatha, Chyrstal, and Elizabeth Bundesen, Ben Lashes, Heather Taylor, Kia Kamran, Julianne Freund, Molly Alward, Todd Thorson, Michael Morris, Wynn Rankin, Michelle Clair, Lia Brown, April Whitney, Albee Dalbotten, Ryan Cunningham, Liza Algar, Paul Myers, Peter Perez, Mike Adkins, Angela Bundesen, Betty Smith, Pokey, Shaggy, and Grumpy's Frienemies everywhere!

ISBN 978-0-545-92651-5

12 11 10 9 8 7 6 5 4 3 2 1          17 18 19 20/0

Printed in the U.S.A.                          40

First Scholastic printing, December 2015

STOCK IMAGE CREDITS:
p. 48-9 Dream Master / Shutterstock.com

Dedicated to the most useful
word in the world:

**NO**

# SAYING "YES" IS OVERRATED.

**IF YOU REALLY WANT TO GET NOTHING DONE, JUST SAY ONE MAGIC WORD:**

# THIS BOOK CONTAINS ALL OF MY LEAST FAVORITE THINGS. CONSIDER IT YOUR GUIDE TO EVERYTHING YOU NEED TO NO.

## WHY NO?

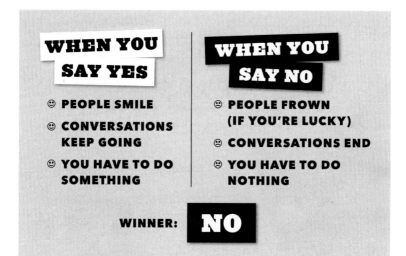

**WHEN YOU SAY YES**

- ☺ PEOPLE SMILE
- ☺ CONVERSATIONS KEEP GOING
- ☺ YOU HAVE TO DO SOMETHING

**WHEN YOU SAY NO**

- ☹ PEOPLE FROWN (IF YOU'RE LUCKY)
- ☹ CONVERSATIONS END
- ☹ YOU HAVE TO DO NOTHING

WINNER: **NO**

## NOW STOP ASKING QUESTIONS AND TAKE THE "NO-IT-ALL" OATH:

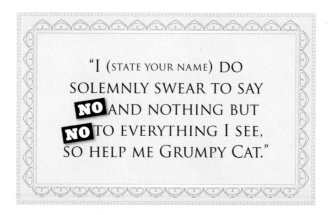

"I (STATE YOUR NAME) DO SOLEMNLY SWEAR TO SAY **NO** AND NOTHING BUT **NO** TO EVERYTHING I SEE, SO HELP ME GRUMPY CAT."

# Butterflies

You see a wonder of nature.
**I SEE A STUPID FLYING BUG
SHOWING OFF.**

I LIKED YOU BETTER IN THE COCOON.

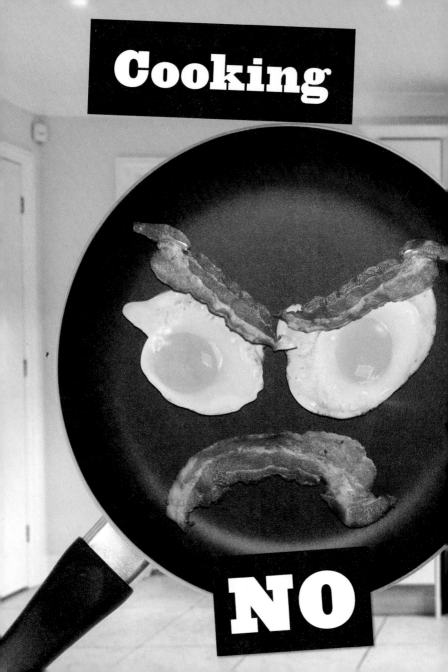

# Flowers

**NO**

**NO**

**NO**

**NO**

**LESS POLLINATING**

**MORE STINGING.**

**Flying**

**NO**

**NEW ADVENTURES ARE THE WORST.**

THIS BABY IS OKAY, THOUGH.

**I MADE ART ONCE**

**IT WAS TERRIBLE**

# Amusement Parks

# GRUMPY'S

## NO-LLER COASTER

**NO**

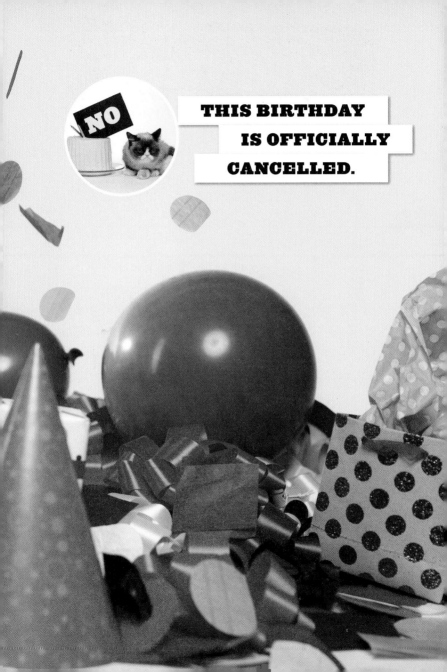

NO

THIS BIRTHDAY IS OFFICIALLY CANCELLED.

# Cuddling

**YOU KEEP TRYING.**

**I KEEP SCRATCHING.**

## SUNDAY

SPORTS ARE ON, PROBABLY. I JUST REMIND MYSELF THAT HALF THE TEAMS LOSE.

## MONDAY

EVERYONE IS MISERABLE. GOAL: MAKE EVERY DAY A MONDAY.

## TUESDAY

NOT MONDAY.

## WEDNESDAY

EVEN FURTHER FROM MONDAY.

## THURSDAY

ALMOST FRIDAY. PEOPLE SEEM ... HOPEFUL? UGH.

## FRIDAY

THE WORST.

## SATURDAY

I REFUSE TO OPEN MY EYES ON THIS DAY BUT I ASSUME IT'S TERRIBLE, TOO.

# Swimming

# Grumpy

ISSUE: WHATEVER

WHY DON'T YOU JUS

# NOTHING IMPOR

*Grumpy Cat is on a mission to "NO" everything.*

#  NO Gazette

YOUR OWN BUSINESS?       EST · 2012

# ...NT HAPPENED

## GRUMPY CAT WALKS OUT OF INTERVIEW

Too bored to continue," says World-Famous Frowning Feline.

## SMILES MUST BE STOPPED

*says International Committee on the Elimination of Smiles.*

Source: I.C.E.S.

# Movies

**EXCEPTION:**

**RUNNING AWAY FROM SOMEONE ANNOYING.**

**Presents**

# Driving

NO

NO

NO

NO

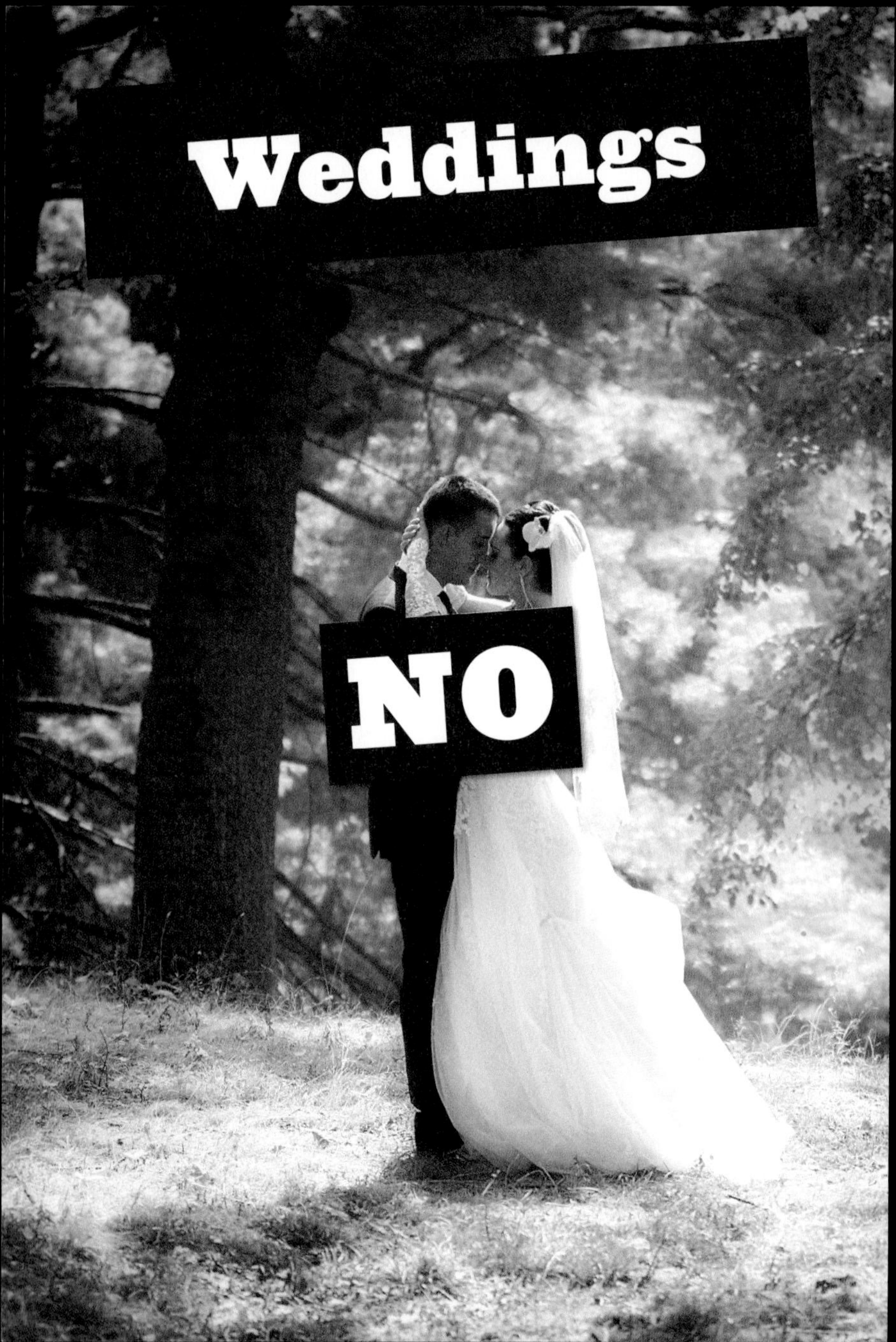
Weddings
NO

**I NOW PRONOUNCE YOU**

**BORING AND ANNOYING**

# Fashion

## THEN

NO

**NOW**

realgrumpycat

1hr

**realgrumpycat** No

# History

**NO**

**NO**

**NO**

MY SOUNDTRACK

IS SILENCE.

# Television

**Mornings**

**NO**

**THE EARLY BIRD GETS**

**ANNOYING QUICKLY**

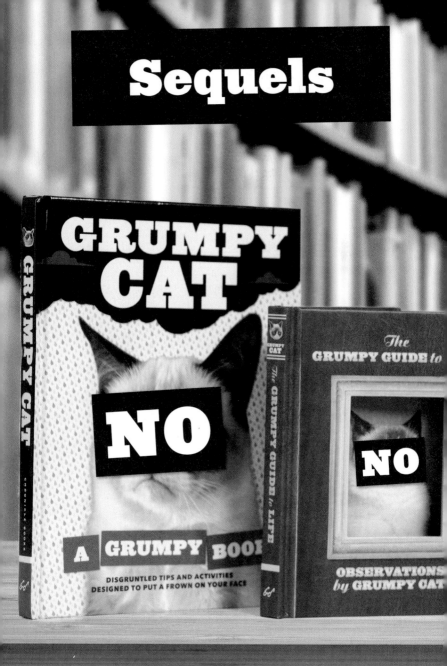

# Sequels

GRUMPY CAT

**NO**

A GRUMPY BOOK

DISGRUNTLED TIPS AND ACTIVITIES
DESIGNED TO PUT A FROWN ON YOUR FACE

The GRUMPY GUIDE to LIFE

**NO**

OBSERVATIONS
by GRUMPY CAT

BEING FAMOUS

IS BORING.

NO NO NO

YOU'RE TERRIBLE.

**Dogs**

**NO**

THIS IS WHAT A BASKET OF BAD BREATH LOOKS LIKE.

NO

NO

# Any Cute Animals, Really

**DUCKLING** NO

**KOALAS** NO NO

**HEDGEHOG** NO

# The Internet

< > ⟳ no. **NO** .no

🔍 NO

THINKING OF YOU

IT'S TERRIBLE

IF YOU'RE HAPPY AND YOU KNOW IT

GET AWAY FROM ME

FROWN AND THE WHOLE WORLD FROWNS WITH YOU.

I HAD FUN ONC

IT WAS AWFU

NO gle

**QUIT WHILE YOU'RE AHEAD.**
Quit while you're behind.
The important thing to remember is this: **QUIT.**

THERE'S NO "I" IN TEAM

THERE'S NO "YOU" EITHER

PUT YOUR BEST **FROWN** FORWARD

EENY

MEENY

MINY

NO

OH, *THIS* ISN'T A MAGIC TRICK.

# Balloons

NO

THIS DID NOT
END WELL.

GET ME OUT OF HERE.

WAIT. I SHOULD BE SQUISHING YOU.

# Fairy Tales

Once upon a

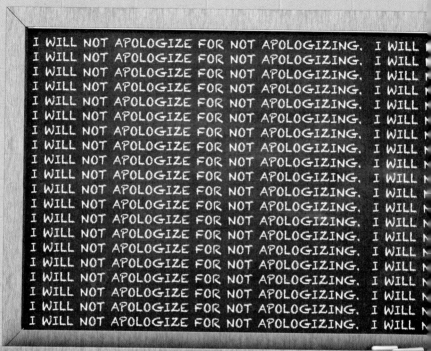

I WILL NOT APOLOGIZE FOR NOT APOLOGIZING. I WILL
I WILL NOT APOLOGIZE FOR NOT APOLOGIZING. I WILL
I WILL NOT APOLOGIZE FOR NOT APOLOGIZING. I WILL
I WILL NOT APOLOGIZE FOR NOT APOLOGIZING. I WILL
I WILL NOT APOLOGIZE FOR NOT APOLOGIZING. I WILL
I WILL NOT APOLOGIZE FOR NOT APOLOGIZING. I WILL
I WILL NOT APOLOGIZE FOR NOT APOLOGIZING. I WILL
I WILL NOT APOLOGIZE FOR NOT APOLOGIZING. I WILL
I WILL NOT APOLOGIZE FOR NOT APOLOGIZING. I WILL
I WILL NOT APOLOGIZE FOR NOT APOLOGIZING. I WILL
I WILL NOT APOLOGIZE FOR NOT APOLOGIZING. I WILL
I WILL NOT APOLOGIZE FOR NOT APOLOGIZING. I WILL
I WILL NOT APOLOGIZE FOR NOT APOLOGIZING. I WILL
I WILL NOT APOLOGIZE FOR NOT APOLOGIZING. I WILL
I WILL NOT APOLOGIZE FOR NOT APOLOGIZING. I WILL
I WILL NOT APOLOGIZE FOR NOT APOLOGIZING. I WILL
I WILL NOT APOLOGIZE FOR NOT APOLOGIZING. I WILL
I WILL NOT APOLOGIZE FOR NOT APOLOGIZING. I WILL
I WILL NOT APOLOGIZE FOR NOT APOLOGIZING. I WILL

**MY HOMEWORK**

**ATE THE DOG.**

# Dreams

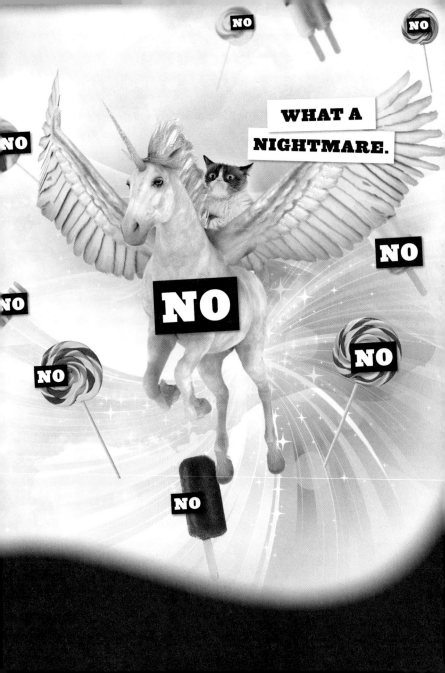

# Crowds

# Hide-and-Seek

# NO

# Big Finishes

NEVER SAY
GOODBYE.

THE SAME
GOES FOR
HELLO.

**NO**

**Too many colors.**

**Leprechauns are the *worst*.**

 **NO THE WORLD**

**SPREAD THE GRUMP
IN THREE EASY STEPS:**

 **FIND SOMETHING YOU
DON'T LIKE.**

 **PUT A NO STICKER
ON IT.**

 **REPEAT.**

**(BONUS POINTS IF YOU HIDE AND
THEN THROW THINGS AT PEOPLE
WHO STOP TO READ YOUR STICKER.)**

# Rainbows

**Storm is ending.**

I REFUSE
TO PARTICIPATE.